THE GREAT RACE

The Building of the Transcontinental Railroad

by Cynthia Mercati

Perfection Learning®

Cover & Inside Illustration: Margaret Sanfilippo
Design: Emily J. Greazel

About the Author

Cynthia Mercati is a writer and a professional actress. She has written many plays for a children's theatre that tours and performs at various schools. She also appears in many of the plays herself.

Ms. Mercati loves reading about history and visiting historical places. When she writes a historical play or book, she wants her readers to feel like they are actually living the story.

Ms. Mercati also loves baseball. Her favorite team is the Chicago White Sox. She grew up in Chicago, Illinois, but she now lives in Des Moines, Iowa. Ms. Mercati has two children and one dog.

Image Credits: ArtToday (some images copyright www.arttoday.com) pp. 4, 7, 10, 11, 14 (top), 20, 21, 27, 33, 34, 36, 40, 47, 52, 54; Library of Congress p. 8; MapArt p. 12; Utah State Historical Society pp. 6, 14, 46, 49; Minnesota Historical Society p. 15; Denver Public Library, Western History Department pp. 23, 28, 29, 39.

Printed in the United States of America. For information, contact Perfection Learning® Corporation, 1000 North Second Avenue, P.O. Box 500, Logan, Iowa 51546-0500.
Phone: 1-800-831-4190 • Fax: 1-800-543-2745
perfectionlearning.com
Paperback ISBN 0-7891-5604-0
Cover Craft® ISBN 0-7569-0343-2
2 3 4 5 6 7 PP 09 08 07 06 05 04

CONTENTS

Chapter 1

The End of the Line

Do you like races? Well, this is the story of one of the longest races in history. It's about the race to build the transcontinental railroad.

My name is Clancy Sullivan. I worked on the Central Pacific branch of the railroad. So did my two friends, Frank Riley and Mike McNamara.

The three of us had just come from Ireland. We were looking for a new life. We were willing to work hard to get it. And that's just what we had to do on the Central Pacific.

Trains meeting at Promontory Point, Utah

On May 10, 1869, two railroads connected in Promontory Point, Utah. They linked the western part of the country with the eastern part.

I can remember that day like it was yesterday. The sky was clear. The American flag snapped in the wind. A band played. Reporters from every big paper in the country were there.

A group of soldiers stood on one side of the tracks. Their brass buttons gleamed in the sun.

Hundreds of Irishmen lined the other side of the tracks. Hundreds of Chinese workers were there too. We were the men who'd built the railroad.

Everyone was looking down the tracks. Some were looking east. Some were looking west. We were all waiting for the trains to arrive. When they did, the big celebration would begin.

The Chinese workers were called **coolies**. Some say the word comes from the Chinese words meaning "rent" and "muscle." Others say the word comes from a Hindu word meaning "unskilled worker."

The Irish workers were called Paddies. Paddy is the Irish nickname for "Patrick."

Jupiter train, carrying the golden spike, on its way to Promontory Point, Utah.

I couldn't wait for the trains to get there. "What's keeping them?" I asked.

Mike laughed. "Who knows?"

Who knows was right! We'd been building the railroad for almost seven years. We'd faced all kinds of trouble. Who knew what could have gone wrong now?

All at once, we heard the Central Pacific come chugging down the line. A mighty cheer went up.

Then a shrill whistle split the air. The Union Pacific came pounding into sight. Another cheer went up.

The two **locomotives** stopped at the very end of the tracks. There was only a rail length between them. All the **ties** had been laid but one.

The race was over. But who had won? Who had laid the most track? Was it the Central Pacific or the Union Pacific?

I'm not telling. Not yet anyway. To find out, you'll have to read to the end of the story—just as we laid those tracks to the end of the line.

Chapter 2

From Sea to Shining Sea

In 1829, the first English locomotive arrived in New York City.

It didn't go very fast. And it didn't go very far.

People who saw it said it looked like a giant grasshopper. But it started people thinking. Maybe we could build our own locomotives.

Railroad companies were formed. Tracks were laid. Soon, railroad lines covered the eastern United States.

But the tracks stopped at the Mississippi River. There weren't enough people living in the West to make a railroad pay.

In 1861, the Civil War broke out. The Northern states were fighting the Southern ones. The South wanted the West to join in the fight. California was especially needed with its gold and silver mines.

President Abraham Lincoln wanted to keep the West united with the North. He decided that a railroad was the way to do it.

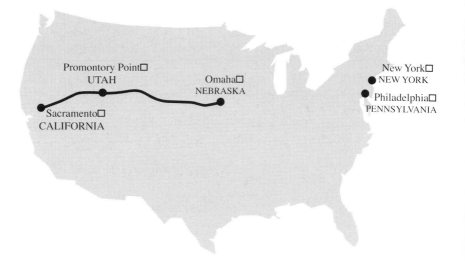

This railroad would run from east to west—from sea to shining sea! It would tie California to the Northern states.

The Union Pacific would start in Omaha, Nebraska. It would build west toward California.

The Central Pacific would start in Sacramento, California. It would build east toward Omaha. The two lines would meet somewhere in Nevada or Utah. No one knew exactly where.

The Union Pacific and the Central Pacific began work in 1863.

The government made a promise to the railroads. For every mile of track they put down, they would be given money and land.

That promise started the great mileage race.

The newspapers picked up the story. Every day, they told their readers how much track the railroads had put down. People made bets on which line would win.

The railroad owners wanted to win the land and money. But we, the men who built the railroads, had a different goal. We wanted to claim the title of greatest track layers in the world.

We were racing for pride.

Chapter 3

Gandy Dancers and Iron Men

Charles Crocker

Charles Crocker was the superintendent of the Central Pacific. He hired all the workers.

Mr. Crocker was a big man. He bellowed like a bull. But he had a kind heart.

While we worked on the tracks, the work train was our home.

A long line of wooden houses had been built on **flatcars**. They were attached to the work train. Inside, the houses were lined with bunks. That's where we slept.

The work train also had kitchen cars. That's where we ate. And we sure did eat hearty!

Platters of meat and potatoes were served at every meal, including breakfast. A big wooden bucket of coffee sat on every table. We dipped our own cups into the bucket.

We got up at dawn. All of our water had
to be hauled in barrels. So we didn't waste
much of it on washing!

We dressed in cotton shirts and sturdy
jeans. Then we tied kerchiefs around our
necks. We wore broad-brimmed hats and big,
thick boots.

The surveyors mapped out the route. The men called *graders* made the roadbed smooth. They cut down trees and dug out rocks.

The bridge monkeys worked with the graders. They built trestles, or bridges, over rivers and canyons.

Next came the joint-tie men. They worked in pairs. Every 14 feet they laid down a wooden railroad tie.

After the joint-tie men came the fillers. They also worked in pairs. Their job was to make sure the ties were ready for the **rails**.

The iron rails were loaded from the work train onto carts. The rails were 28 feet long. Each one weighed about 700 pounds.

Mules pulled the carts to the **railhead**. Then the trackmen went to work. That's what Frank, Mike, and I were. Rust eaters, they called us. We called ourselves iron men!

"Away she goes!" the boss would yell. Two trackmen would grab the end of the rail. They'd start forward. The rest of the **gang** would take hold of the rail. We'd move it forward until it was clear of the cart.

"Down!" the boss would yell. We'd drop the rail in place on top of the wooden ties. We could lay down a rail in less than 30 seconds!

After the trackmen came the spikers. They drove six **spikes** to hold the rails to the ties. Then they screwed heavy iron clamps to each side of the rails.

The track liners moved in quickly. They were also called *gandy dancers*. They used crowbars to make sure the tracks formed a strong, straight line.

The most popular workers were the water carriers. They passed out cups of cool water from their buckets.

We iron men sang as we worked. We made up our own songs. Our favorite was "Drill, Ye Tarriers, Drill."

Some people said the Irish workers were digging their way across the country like terrier dogs. With our Irish accents, the word sounded more like *tarrier*. That's where the name came from.

We sang our songs to match the rhythm of our work. It sure made the days go faster.

Chapter 4

Crocker's Pets

The Central Pacific soon faced its biggest problem. The mountains!

The Sierra Nevada was 150 miles wide. These mountains rose 7,000 feet above Sacramento. Their walls were solid rock.

How were we supposed to build a railroad through that?

Mike had the answer. "With shovels, wheelbarrows, mules, muscles, and sweat!"

The railroad couldn't go over the mountains. They were too steep.

And the railroad couldn't go around them. The tracks would have to wind great distances to reach the other side.

That meant we'd have to build tunnels. We'd have to cut shelves into the rock.

Mr. Crocker needed thousands of men to do all this work. He put out ads all over California.

But most of the men who came west wanted to get rich quick. They were seeking their fortunes in the goldfields or silver mines.

Sierra Nevada

Crocker didn't know what to do. We were losing the race to the Union Pacific.

Then one day, Crocker got an idea. He was using Irish immigrants to build the Central Pacific. Why not use Chinese immigrants too?

Thousands of Chinese had come to California looking for gold. But the white settlers wouldn't allow them into the goldfields.

Instead, the Chinese had to be laundrymen, peddlers, waiters, and cooks. Those jobs didn't pay much. So they were eager to work on the railroad.

Crocker hired 50 Chinese men from Sacramento. They rode in a freight car to the railhead.

When the rest of us saw them, we thought it was a joke. They were all short and thin.

Railroad workers

"They're too skinny to work on the railroad," Mike called out in his booming voice.

The Chinese workers wore blue jackets and baggy blue pants. Their braided pigtails hung neatly down their backs.

On their heads were straw hats. These were shaped like triangles and looked like baskets. The hats were called *coolie hats*.

The first time
we saw those hats,
we laughed out
loud. We never
stopped to think
how funny our
clothes must have
looked to the Chinese!

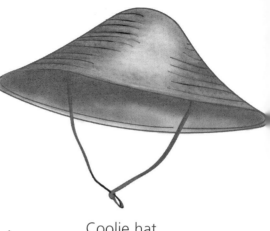

Coolie hat

The Chinese men worked quickly and quietly. They stopped only long enough to sip a cup of tea.

By the end of the day, they'd done even more work than Mr. Crocker had asked them to.

"I guess I have to eat my words," Mike said. "Those Chinese lads are fine workers indeed!"

More Chinese were sent for at once. Soon, thousands worked on the Central Pacific. They came to be called Crocker's Pets.

But for all the Chinese did, they weren't treated very well. They were paid less than the rest of us.

They weren't allowed to sleep on the work train. So they set up tents and slept on the ground.

They were given the hardest jobs. Other workers often treated them badly.

One day Mike, Frank, and I heard a crew of surveyors teasing some Chinese workers.

"That stuff you coolies eat looks like weeds," a tall, red-faced man said.

His friends all laughed. "Why don't you eat some American food? Then maybe you'll grow a little. You look like drowned rats now!"

The Chinese men didn't answer. They just stood there quietly. Their heads were bowed. They needed these jobs. They didn't want to start trouble.

Mike walked up to the man who had spoken. Frank and I were right behind him.

"You leave these fellows alone!" Mike commanded.

The red-faced surveyor glared at Mike. He probably thought about letting his fists do the talking.

One of his pals nudged him. He must have noticed our track-laying muscles.

Quickly the surveyors turned around. They walked away.

"We should be glad the Chinese are here," Mike called after them. "We can't build this railroad without them!"

Chapter 5

The Mountain Challenge

Up, up, up the mountains the Central Pacific railroad went. With **picks** and shovels, the basket-hatted Chinese chipped away at the rock.

Sometimes we had to blast our way through the mountains. The Chinese did most of this dangerous work.

Chinese railroad worker carrying water buckets

They balanced long bamboo poles across their shoulders. On each end of the pole hung a keg of blasting powder.

Holes were drilled into the rock. Powder was poured into them. Fuses were then slipped into the holes.

The fuses were lit. All the crews ran for cover. The blasts echoed through the mountains.

Shovelful by shovelful, the broken rock was loaded into carts. Cartload by cartload, it was dumped into canyons to fill them up.

Sometimes the canyons were too deep to fill. Then trestles had to be built across them.

Finally, we came up against a wall with a sheer cliff. It dropped straight down for a thousand feet. Not even powder would work here! A roadbed would have to be dug into the face of the cliff. But how? Our Chinese workers came up with the answer.

They wove baskets out of thin strips of wood. The baskets were small but strong.

We tied ropes to the baskets. One at a time, the Chinese workers got into the baskets. In their hands were hammers and **chisels**.

The Irish Paddies stood atop the mountain. We held on to the ropes.

Down, down, down the Chinese workers went.

The baskets spun and dipped in the wind. But the brave-hearted Chinese kept chipping away at the mountain.

"Those men have guts," Mike said. The rest of us nodded.

Suddenly, one of the ropes broke. The basket crashed down the mountainside. The cries of the men echoed back to us.

And then the cries stopped. The men were dead.

Everyone was quiet. We felt bad. Mr. Crocker was sad—and worried.

Would the rest of the Chinese refuse to go on? Would work on the Central Pacific grind to a stop?

No! The basket men kept at their job. All day the clink of hammers and chisels sounded. Stone chips rattled as they fell down the mountain.

The Chinese workers carved out a ledge. They made it wide enough for us to lay track.

We'd won the battle against the mountain!

Chapter 6

Through Ice and Snow

Summer passed. Winter closed in.

Cold winds howled around the mountains. Snow fell.

Steam plows pushed up the mountainside. Behind them came sleds, loaded with supplies.

Soon, the snow got deeper. The plows couldn't get through.

Deep snow stopping the train

Mr. Crocker sent most of us back to Sacramento. My friends and I were mighty glad to go. We couldn't wait to get warm again.

Mr. Crocker kept a handful of Chinese workers.

When we returned we heard about their hard winter. During the summer, we had started building a tunnel through the mountains. All through the cold winter, the small group of Chinese kept working on it.

They dug narrow passageways under the hard-packed snow. Like earthworms, they crawled through the passageways to get to the tunnel. Spring came. Avalanches thundered down the mountain. A crew of workers got caught in the path of one. They were swept away.

We found the men months later, down in the valley. They were still standing, frozen stiff. Their picks were still in their hands. They'd given their all to the Central Pacific.

Chapter 7

The Iron Horse

At last it was summer. Back we came—back to win the race.

We made it through the mountains! Then we started laying tracks across the Nevada desert.

The sun hung above us, big and yellow. We baked in the heat.

Dust rose in clouds. It burned our eyes. It dried our throats. But on we went, putting down iron. Nothing could stop us.

On the other side of the country, the Union Pacific had its own problems.

The Union Pacific was building its route west. It went right through Sioux hunting grounds.

For years, white men had been pushing Native Americans farther and farther west. From the Atlantic coast to Ohio and Illinois. Then across the Mississippi. Finally, out to the Plains.

The Indians called the railroad the Iron Horse.

Now the Iron Horse was pushing them farther still. The Indians decided to fight for their land.

When the first surveyors came out, the Indians attacked them. The Indians won against these small bands of men.

But the railroad crews got bigger and bigger. Every man was given a rifle and ammunition.

At the first sign of Indians, an alarm was sounded. The crews dropped their tools. They grabbed their rifles. Many of the workers were ex-soldiers from the Civil War. They knew all about fighting.

They jumped into the holes they'd been digging for track. Or they took shelter behind railroad cars. Then they fired away.

The Native Americans fought hard. But they were greatly outnumbered. Their weapons were not strong enough. They saw that their way of life was doomed.

In 1868, the Native Americans signed several treaties. These gave the Union Pacific the right to cross their land.

Indians were not the only dangers the Union Pacific faced. Many men died of disease. And many accidents happened.

No one knows how many lives were lost in the struggle to build a railroad across America.

Railroad crews and the Native Americans

chapter 8

The Ten-Mile Day

The two railroads were getting closer. Americans were getting more excited. Who would win the mileage race?

It was finally decided that the two railroads would meet at Promontory Point. Now we knew where we were racing to!

We heard that the Union Pacific was laying three miles of track a day. Then they laid four, then five. Finally, we heard they were laying six!

The men on the Central Pacific got going. We laid seven miles of track in one day!

The Union Pacific answered back. They put down seven and a half!

Mr. Crocker bragged that his men could lay ten miles of track in one day.

"Impossible!" Americans said. "No human beings can lay ten miles of track in one day!"

But Mr. Crocker was sure his men could do it. So were we!

Crocker asked for volunteers for the ten-mile day. Five thousand men stepped forward.

From those, Mr. Crocker selected 1,400 men. He picked 8 of his best rust eaters to lay down the rails.

Frank, Mike, and I were among the eight!

Every volunteer was promised four times his normal wages if we could meet the challenge.

It was 7 a.m. on April 29, 1869. A whistle pierced the cold morning air. That was the signal we'd been waiting for. The ten-mile day began.

"Let's go, men!" Mr. Crocker yelled. "Let's show 'em!"

The trackmen knew that everything depended on us. We didn't take a moment to rest. We worked in two crews of four. Every 20 seconds, we laid down a rail!

Dust swirled around us. The sound of clanking iron filled the air.

The eight of us were panting and sweating. But we kept up our pace all morning. The other gangs worked in relay teams. But the eight iron men didn't use any substitutes.

At 1:30, Crocker shouted to us. "Lay off!"

The eight of us fell on the ground. We were gasping for breath. We wolfed down lunch. We drank water in great gulps.

"Do you need to be spelled for a bit?" Crocker asked us.

"No, sir," Mike answered for all of us. "We can lay rail forever!"

We started up again. Now the route was all uphill. I felt like I was a machine. But I kept on. I was too tired to think and too tired to feel. But I kept working. We all did!

Forward we ran, carrying the rails. Each crew worked together as if four men were one.

At 7 p.m., the whistle blew again. Crocker signaled for us to stop. He made an announcement.

"You have indeed just laid ten miles of track!" he exclaimed. "Plus another 1,800 feet for good measure."

A cheer went up from everyone watching. The gangs flung their hats into the air.

I was almost too tired to move. For once, Mike was too tired to talk!

A total of 3,520 rails had been laid. The eight rust eaters had each lifted more than 125 tons of iron.

We'd done the impossible! And we'd set a record that has never been beaten.

chapter 9

The Golden Spike

It had been 6¹/₂ years, 3 months, and 29 days since we started. Finally, the railroad was done.

It was a big day at Promontory Point. Men in fancy black coats stepped off the Central Pacific. More officials climbed down from the Union Pacific. They shook hands.

Two Chinese workers put the last tie in place. They placed the last rails on the tie. The only thing left to do was drive in the last four spikes. Two were silver. One was a mixture of silver and gold. They were quickly driven in.

Then the last spike was put in place. It was pure gold!

The Governor of California was handed a silver **sledgehammer**. He swung at the golden spike. He missed.

The vice-president of the Union Pacific picked up the sledgehammer. He swung hard. He missed too!

All the watching men burst into laughter. I whispered to my friends, "That'll show 'em how hard it is to build a railroad."

An ordinary crewman was called over. He was handed the sledgehammer. With one blow, he drove in the golden spike!

The last spike is put in place.

The transcontinental railroad was officially finished. Telegraph wires flashed the message across the country. From coast to coast, people celebrated.

But who had won the great race?

The Union Pacific had laid 555 miles of track. The Central Pacific had laid 549 miles.

The race was called a draw!

My friends and I always believed the Central Pacific had really won. So did most people.

After all, we'd had the hardest job. We'd had to cut our way through the mountains. We'd had to cross the desert in summer.

Bret Harte wrote a poem to honor the big day in Promontory Point.

What was it the engines said,
Pilots touching,—head to head,
Facing on the single track,
Half a world behind each back?

Maybe, I thought, the engines were saying thank you to the men who'd built the railroad. We'd put in years of muscle and sweat. But it had been worth it.

Our country was now joined together by an unbroken band of iron.

Chapter 10

A Country United

Clancy, Frank, and Mike are not real people. But their story is a true one. The things they did were done by the thousands of Irish immigrants who worked on the Central Pacific and the Union Pacific.

The eight iron men who laid the rails on the ten-mile day were all Irish.

Before the transcontinental railroad, the United States had been just a group of loosely connected sections. East, West, North, and South.

After the railroad was built, travel became easier and quicker. People could cross the country to seek new opportunities. We really became a nation united.

Now people fly across the United States in a few hours. They soar into space! Our modern-day travels would amaze all those graders, gandy dancers, spikers, and rust eaters.

But never forget, the transcontinental railroad did it first!

"Drill, Ye Tarriers, Drill"

Every morning about seven o'clock,
There were twenty tarriers drilling at the rock.
The boss comes along and he says,
"Keep still
And bear down heavy on the cast iron drill."

Chorus

And drill, ye tarriers, drill,
Drill, ye tarriers, drill.
For it's work all day for the sugar in yer tay (tea),
Down beyond the railway.
And drill, ye tarriers, drill.

And blast and fire.
The foreman's name is John McCann.
By God, he is a blamed mean man.
One day a premature blast went off,
And a mile in the air went big Jim Goff.

Chorus

When next payday came around,
Jim Goff a dollar short was found.
When he asked, "What for?" came this reply,
"You were docked for the time
you were up in the sky."

Chorus

RAILROAD TERMS

The men who worked on the railroad had their own vocabulary. Here are some of the words they used.

chisel   metal tool with a cutting edge at one end used to chip rock

coolie   unskilled laborer from the Far East

flatcar   railroad car without sides, ends, or covering

gang   crew of railroad workers

locomotive   self-propelled vehicle that runs on rails and moves railroad cars

pick   heavy iron tool, pointed at both ends, with a wooden handle

railhead	beginning or end of the railroad line
rails	the iron bars forming a train track
sledgehammer	large heavy hammer that is swung with both hands
spike	large nail used to secure the rails to the ties
tie	wooden support that the rails are fastened to so they stay in line